White On Blonde

texas

Exclusive Distributors

International Music Publications Limited, Southend Road, Woodford Green, Essex IG8 8HN, England

International Music Publications Limited, 25 Rue D'Hautville, 75010 Paris, France

International Music Publications GmbH, Germany, Marstallstraße 8, D-80539 Munchen, Germany

Nuova Carish S.R.L., Via M.F. Quintiliano 40, 20138 Milano, Italy

Danmusik, Vognmagergade 7, DK-1120 Copenhagen K, Denmark

Warner/Chappell Music Inc, Australia, 1 Cassins Avenue, North Sydney, New South Wales 2060, Australia

Folio © 1997 International Music Publications Ltd
Southend Road, Woodford Green, Essex IG8 8HN

Music Transcribed by Barnes Music Engraving Ltd., East Sussex TN22 4HA
Printed by The Panda Group · Haverhill · Suffolk CB9 8PR · UK · Binding by ABS · Cambridge

Photo's Pages 3 & 8 Elaine Constantine, Page 5 Jurgen Teller

The story here is very simple: Texas have been away for a while in order to make an incredible album. And they've done just that.

That's it.

You can spin the story out a bit mind - and if you do the new music Texas have produced becomes just as fascinating as it is unashamedly daring and modern. Try this vision for size: You are 18 years old, your name is Sharleen Spiteri and you're living in a rented flat in Glasgow. The first song you ever write is called "I Don't Want a Lover", ten years later it will still be being played at least once a week on most of Britain's major radio stations. By the time you are 20, your first album has been hanging out healthily in the Top Ten of the British album charts, while escalating sales overseas are knocking your record company sideways. Sure, your best friend and writing partner Johnny McElhone had penned hits for both Altered Images and Hipsway, but this really is something else. All around the world people are coming to the same conclusion: that "the girl in Texas is a brilliant singer". You are the first British band asked to play acoustic for an MTV special.

There are a couple of band changes here and there, but you go on to follow the pat that is now laid out for you - three albums of polished, well crafted songs fusing pop, soul, rock and country. They sell by the bucketload. Your third LP is your best yet, featuring vocal sparring with Sly and the Family Stone's Sister Rose it sees album sales pass a million in France alone. In the US your band is attaining the kind of hip reputation that all great exports now dream of (before Oasis have even written their first single, you have already been given George Harrison's guitar pick and Ringo is proclaiming himself "a huge fan" in the press). The homeboy's favourite designer, Tommy Hilfiger, wants to sponsor your tours and Ellen Degeneres, star of the massive sitcom *Ellen*, pays serious money to use a selection of your songs, "So Called Friend", as her programme's intro music.

Back in Britain, meanwhile, your last big chart hit is a cover version of the Al Green song, "Tired of Being Alone". The soul tune has only been released following a surprisingly rapturous reception on being played at a low key, press only concert at London's Ronnie Scotts club. Something strange is going on. The music you and your band is now drawing on is more likely to have descended from the houses of Shrine, Stax or Salsoul than from the corporate empires of AOR, yet you're still playing packed-out venues around the world to diehard fans crying out for polished, up-tempo Scot Pop. Time to withdraw and to redraw the game plan.

In 1994, Texas started writing and recording a fourth album. At the time of its inception, their sound was potentially a musical muddle - rock or soul? pop or roots? - yet there was also the potential there for things to now be taken to another level altogether. Sharleen had been spending a lot of time living in Paris, while the rest of the band had completed a home studio track in Glasgow.

The band now buried themselves there, constantly writing and recording and heatedly debating the relative production merits of DJ Premier versus The RZA. This was the first time Texas had really re-thought sound, although events were hardly slowing to anything like a crawl. In one week late in 1995 for example, Sharleen Spiteri found herself flying to Hollywood to record a personal appearance for Ellen (the show was using snatches of Texas music throughout episodes), before jetting back to Manchester to work with her band alongside the young dynamic Grand Central crew (on a collaborative hip hop/soul project), then driving across the country to Glasgow to appear at a farewell gig by acclaimed country rockers The Jayhawks (Sharleen had provided vocals on one song on their second and final album). This was a schizophrenic work schedule by anyone's standards. As Sharleen wrote yet more songs for the forthcoming fourth Texas album, she was drawing on an incredible array of experiences - this wasn't the life of some indie Britpop babe, but could those other spiky sirens really compete with this?

And so to the big question: Texas, just a band of angular, modern contradictions, or a modern band now ready to contradict the preconceptions of all the rest? From a comfortable list of more than twenty killer new songs, Texas have shaped a commercial album of classic proportions. Spanning the full spectrum of their musical world, from Marvin Gaye to John Lennon, from the Wu Tang Clan and TLC to Fleetwood Mac and The Pretenders, this is an album to be reckoned with.

Recorded and produced largely in Glasgow, it also features collaborative work with producer Mike Hedges (responsible for the fantastic strings on the recent Manic Street Preachers' LP with the Grand Central duo Rae & Christian and with Dave Stewart (the ex-Eurythmic beardie). And yes, those styles and flavours can all co-exist on one record. During the week of this press biography being written, one new Texas track "Good Advice" got its first airing on promo on Manchester's Kiss FM. "Is that really the same Texas?" quized one panelist on the *Drivetime Hit or Miss*? slot. He and his colleagues then pronounced the tune a unanimous hit. Interestingly, that same day, one member of Texas (guitarist Ally McErlane) was in Paris appearing in a celebrity studded Pret a Porter catwalk show, while back in London the new issue of The Face magazine was just hitting the shelves with Texas' contribution to the hyped new "Central Heating" LP namechecked as the record's highpoint.

The return of Texas is ready and word is already out. Now go figure.

say what you want

Twenty seconds on the back time
I feel you're on the run
Never lived too long to make right
I see you're doing fine
And when I get that feeling
I can no longer slide I can no longer run
And when I get that feeling
I can no longer hide for it's no longer fun

Well you can say what you want
But it won't change my mind
I'll feel the same about you
And you can tell me your reasons
But it won't change my feelings
I'll feel the same about you

What I am is what you want to be
Now that I'm not there
Took the tables away from you
It's turned and I don't care
And when I get that feeling
I can no longer slide I can no longer run
And when I get that feeling
I can no longer hide for it's no longer fun

Well you can say what you want
But it won't change my mind
I'll feel the same about you
And you can tell me your reasons
But it won't change my feelings
I'll feel the same about you

I've said goodnight try to sleep tight
Just dream of me
Go close your eyes cause I've closed mine
The sun will shine from time to time
When you dream of me

Well you can say what you want
But it won't change my mind
I'll feel the same about you
And you can tell me your reasons
But it won't change my feelings
I'll feel the same about you

drawing crazy patterns

It's like he's sleeping now
He got married in a rush
8 months on and summer's gone
He finds it hard to adjust
He's feeling younger now
Younger than he was before
He wishes he could change his mind
Old mistakes they seem so small
And if he had to be you
Then he'd get out and do the things he's always wanted

Standing outside like a joker on a hill
He's drawing crazy patterns with his shoes

Some people push by
And everyone is cursing them
But he doesn't raise his hand
He broke his dreams and lost a friend
He's asking questions now
Caught in his confusion
He shakes his head and looks at me
Then he shouts out loud
If you had to be me
Would you get out and do the things you've always wanted

Standing outside like a joker on a hill
He's drawing crazy patterns with his shoes

It's like he's sleeping now
When you're gazing at the floor
And on this late night
It's getting harder now, harder now

Standing outside like a joker on a hill
He's drawing crazy patterns with his shoes

halo

Bright light city
You're her religion
Superstars in their own private movie
Play just like children
Lies that take her
Places she's never seen
The kiss and tell of it all
To her it seems so obscene
She's so pretty her hair is a mess
We all love her
To that we confess

She has a halo
We really do adore her
For she has a halo
Can we touch her

For their blindness she sees much further
Like on a wide screen viewing going down on her
She's so pretty her hair is a mess
We all love her
To that we confess

She has a halo
We really do adore her
For she has a halo
Can we touch her

She believes in everything
And she believes in nothing, in everything

She has a halo
We really do adore her
For she has a halo
Can we touch her

She believes in everything
And she believes in nothing, in everything
She believes in everything
And she believes in nothing

She has a halo
She has a halo

insane

Somebody told me it was over
Nobody told me where it began
No-one believes in you
I understand
Like a blind man whose lost his way
No-one hears a word of what you say
I forgive you
Would you do the same
I would believe you if only you'd be true
I would believe if it were true

Everybody wants to be a winner
Nobody wants to lose their game
It's the same for me it's the same for you
It's insane

I don't know where you've been looking
I think it's only in you're mind
Tied so tight inside of you all the thoughts unkind
I would believe you if only you'd be true
I would believe if it were true

Cause everybody wants to be a winner
Nobody wants to lose their game
It's the same for me it's the same for you
It's insane

I would believe you if only you'd be true
I'm getting older and I can't escape time

Cause everybody wants to be a winner
Nobody wants to lose their game
It's the same for me
It's the same for you
It's insane

put your arms around me

Are you ready maybe are you willing to run
Are you ready to let yourself drown
Are you holding your breath
Are you ready or not
Are you ready maybe do you long to confess
Do you feel that you're already numb
Are you sure of yourself
Would you lie if you're not
You tire me out don't want to let that happen .
A secret scream so loud why did you let that happen

So put your arms around me
You let me believe that you are someone else
Cause only time can take you
So let me believe that I am someone else

Maybe are you ready to break
Do you think that I push you too far
Would you open yourself
Are you reckless or not
You tire me out don't want to let that happen
A secret scream so loud why did you Let that happen

So put your arms around me
You let me believe that you are someone else
Cause only time can take you
So let me believe that I am someone else
Let me believe that I am somewhere else

So put your arms around me
So put your arms around me
Make me believe
Take me take me somewhere, somewhere
Let me believe
Cause only time can take you so stop

black eyed boy

No I don't lack ambition
Can't you see what I hate
That it's you who is sinking
Locked behind iron gates
You should know, you're falling into fiction
I can tell you're on some foolish mission

Your black eyed soul, you should know
That there's nowhere else to go
My black eyed boy you will find
Your own space and time

You call me superstitious, tie me up with your deceit
I could never be malicious
Though I seem so bittersweet
You should know, you're falling into fiction
I can tell you're on some foolish mission

Your black eyed soul
You should know that there's nowhere else to go
My black eyed boy you will find
Your own space and time

You should know, you're falling into fiction
I can tell you're on some foolish mission

Your black eyed soul you should know
That there's nowhere else to go
My black eyed boy you will find
Your own space and time

white on blonde

A perfect face comes calling
A perfect hand reaches out
Her perfect face in the morning
December girl feels the same
She needs to find a place
'Cause she never looked so good when she was down

She's blonde on white, white on blonde
Her perfections are now one, reflections everywhere
If you gaze for too long it will fade and then it's gone
Reflections everywhere

Imagine naked legs falling
Walking barefoot in the rain
Imagine freezing cold weather
December girl feels the same
She needs to find a place
'Cause she never looked so good when she was down

She's blonde on white, white on blonde
Her perfections are now gone, reflections everywhere
If you gaze for too long it will fade and then it's gone
Reflections everywhere

A perfect face comes calling
A perfect hand reaches out
She needs to find a place

'Cause she never looked so good when she was down

She's blonde on white, white on blonde
Her perfections are now gone, reflections everywhere
If you gaze for too long it will fade and then it's gone
Reflections everywhere

ticket to lie

Attention annoys me I could disappoint
So just take a walk and try to avoid
The cars in the street now they could knock you down
So just take a bus it's a long way down

There's a ticket in my hand
If you want
I don't know what you think

Tell me where you want to go
Take a breath when I ask you to just try
Close your eyes I'll take you there
I could take you anywhere come fly
Tell me what you want to do
And I can make it up for you and lie

Laughter annoys me makes me feel sad
Yes I wrote that book can I have it back
There's black all around me and I'm lost in this crowd
There's no coming back cause I'm on my way down

There's a ticket in my hand
I can't use it without you

So tell me where you want to go
Take a breath when ask you to just try
Close your eyes I'll take you there
I could take you anywhere come fly
Tell me what you want to do
And I can make it up for you and lie

So tell me where you want to go
Take a breath when I ask you to just try
Close your eyes I'll take you there
I could take you anywhere come fly
So tell me where you want to go
Take a breath when I ask you to just try
Tell me what you want to do
And I can make it up for you and lie
So tell me where you want to go
And I will put that ticket in your hand

postcard

I'll send you a postcard from heaven's ocean
I feel like staying here in heaven's ocean

I've been dreaming for days now
Jump in the sea I do that easily
The sound's drowning what I'm seeing
Count everyone for questions I have not known

I'll send you a postcard from heaven's ocean
I feel like staying here in heaven's ocean

There's a storm in my thoughts now
Come wash me clean beneath the waves with me
Now we're smiling see me smiling
Silence is what I need it's only in the sea

I'll send you a postcard from heaven's ocean
I Feel like staying here in heaven's ocean -

good advice

Open the window I need some air
So many people and there's such disorder here
Familiar faces found out lies
And to distract I watch the passers by
I wonder what they'd recognise.
And what they'd recommend to fill my days
Possessions start to wear me down
I need some good advice some good advice to wear my crown

I'm nervous can you help me

Inside they harbour secret thoughts
They peek through windows that have twice been locked
I have to walk to wear me out
I need some good advice some good advice to wear my crown

I'm nervous can you help me

I fold my arms and pray to leave
I've got a headfull of ideas inside of me
My lips pressed tight so as not to drown
I need some good advice some good advice to wear my crown

I'm nervous can you help me

Giving me good advice can never be wrong if I know it's you

breathless

All these bruises keep me awake
I guess I'm just too tired to sleep
God only knows I'm too lost to cry
For kissing liars has kept me true

I'll fall but I'll heal
So hold me tight cause I'm so lonely
I'll fall but I'll heal
So hold me tight cause I'm so lonely

He hates so much his love he says
Inside it's dark I need to smile
He shouts so loud I never hear
That's why the truth's always abused
As I slip into unconsciousness
I never felt so much to blame

I'll fall but I'll heal
So hold me tight cause I'm so lonely
I'll fall but I'll heal
So hold me tight cause I'm so lonely

As I slip into unconsciousness
I never felt so much to blame

I'll fall but I'll heal
So hold me tight cause I'm so lonely
I'll fall but I' ll heal
So hold me tight cause I'm so lonely

polo mint city

Round and round
In polo mint city
Isn't it pretty
In polo mint city

He took my breath away

0.34

Music by Cole Porter

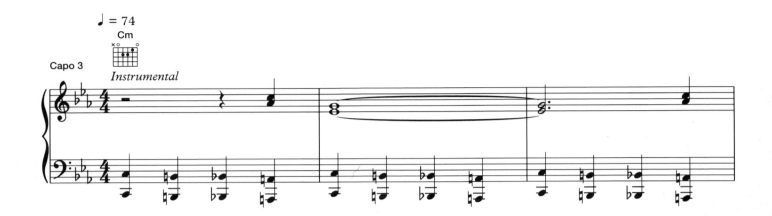

say what you want

Words and Music by
John McElhone and Sharleen Spiteri

Twen-ty sec-onds on the
What I am is what you

back time,_____ I feel you're on the run.
want to be,_____ now that I'm not there.

drawing crazy patterns

Words and Music by
John McElhone and Sharleen Spiteri

It's like he's sleep-ing now, ___ he ___ got mar-ried
Some peo-ple push by and ev-ery-one is

in a rush, ___ eight ___ months on and sum - mer's gone, ___
curs - ing them, ___ but he does - n't raise his hand, ___

he finds it hard ___ to ad - just, ___ he's feel - ing
he broke his dreams and lost a friend, ___ he's ask - ing

halo

Words and Music by
John McElhone and Sharleen Spiteri

Bright light ci - ty, you're her re - li - gion,___ su-per-stars_ in their own

put your arms around me

Words and Music by
John McElhone, Sharleen Spitiri,
Robert Hodgens and Dave Stewart

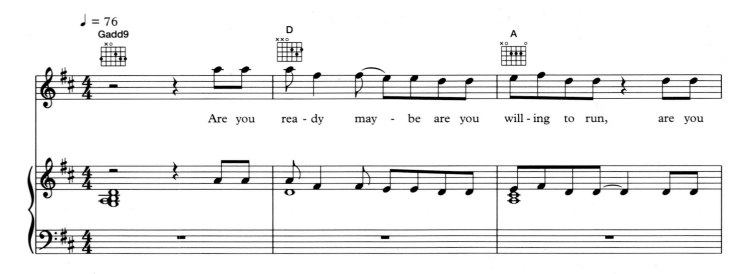

Are you rea-dy may-be are you will-ing to run, are you

rea-dy to let your-self drown,_____ are you hold-ing your breath,_____

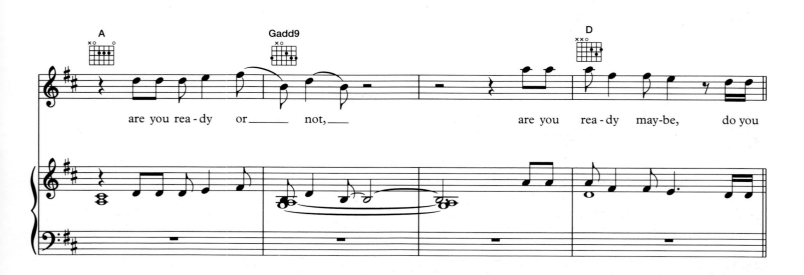

are you rea-dy or_____ not,_____ are you rea-dy may-be, do you

insane

Words and Music by
John McElhone and Sharleen Spiteri

Some-bo-dy told me it was ov - er, no-bo-dy told me where it be - gan, no-one be-lieves in you, I un-der-stand.

black eyed boy

Words and Music by
John McElhone, Sharleen Spiteri,
Edward Campbell, Richard Hynd
and Robert Hodgens

polo mint city

Music by John McElhone and Sharleen Spiteri
Words by John McElhone

white on blonde

Words and Music by
John McElhone and Sharleen Spiteri

A per-fect face comes call-ing,
Im-ag-ine na-ked legs fall-ing,

a per-fect hand reach-es out,___
walk-ing bare-foot in the rain,___

her per-fect face in the morn-
im-ag-ine freez-ing cold wea-

-ing,
-ther,

De-cem-ber girl feels the same,___
De-cem-ber girl feels the same,___

postcard

Words and Music by
John McElhone and Sharleen Spiteri

I'll send you a post-card from hea-ven's o - cean,_____
I'll send you a post-card from hea-ven's o - cean,_____

I feel like stay-ing__ in hea-ven's o - cean.
I feel like stay-ing__ in hea-ven's o - cean.

I've been dream -
There's a storm

I'll send you a post - card from hea-ven's o - cean,_____
I'll send you a post - card from hea-ven's o - cean,_____

and I feel like stay - ing__ in hea-ven's o - cean.
I think I could stay__ here in hea-ven's o - cean.__

D.%. and repeat to fade

0.28

Music by
John McElhone, Sharleen Spitiri

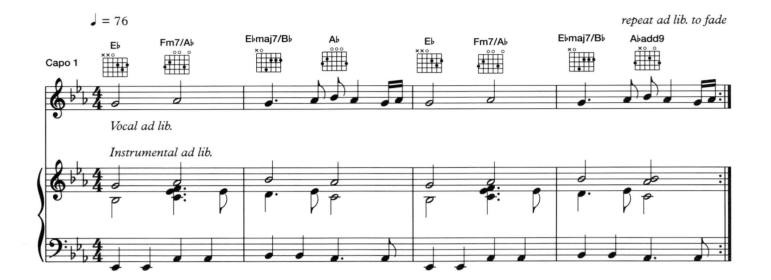

ticket to lie

Words and Music by
John McElhone, Sharleen Spiteri
and Roger Hodgens

good advice

Words and Music by
John McElhone, Sharleen Spitiri,
John Cameron, Mark Rae and Steve Christian

Instrumental

D.%. *al Coda*

⊕ *CODA*

Giv-ing me good ad-vice can ne-ver be__ wrong__ if I know it's__ you.

repeat ad lib.
to fade

Giv-ing me good ad-vice can ne-ver be__ wrong_ if I know it's__ you. Yeah._____

breathless

Words and Music by
John McElhone and Sharleen Spiteri